Section One — Numbers

Calculator Buttons P1

Q1 a) 1   f) 900
b) 4   g) 25
c) 121   h) 1 000 000
d) 256   i) 0
e) 1

Q2 a) 4   f) 20
b) 6   g) 1.732 (to 3 d.p.)
c) 17   h) 2.646 (to 3 d.p.)
d) 0   i) 5.477 (to 3 d.p.)
e) 60

Q3 a) 1   e) 3
b) 0   f) −3
c) 7   g) −4
d) 10   h) −1.710 (to 3 d.p.)

Q4 a) 8.4
b) 0.622 (3 s.f.)
c) 0.0798 (3 s.f.)

Q5 a) 2   d) 29.867 (3 d.p.)
b) 1   e) 0.353 (3 d.p.)
c) 0.333 (3 d.p.)   f) 0.0729 (3 s.f.)

Q6 a) 1   e) 0.5
b) 1 048 576   f) 59 049
c) 1 048 576   g) 26 742 (5 s.f.)
d) 9.870 (3 d.p.)

Q7 a) 0.0833...   c) 0.2294...
b) 0.0243...   d) 1.1547...

Types of Number P2

Q1 4

Q2 -3 °C

Q3 a) $6 \div 2 = 3$, rational
b) $\sqrt{16} = 4$, rational
c) $\sqrt{5} = 2.23606...$, irrational
d) $3 \div 8 = 0.375$, rational
e) $\sqrt[3]{25} = 2.92401...$, irrational
f) Rational

Q4 a) the third cube number (27)
b) the fourth square number (16)

Q5 a) 2
b) e.g. 29
c) 19
d) 19 and 2
e) e.g. 1 or 25

Q6 a)

1	②	③	4	⑤	6	⑦	8	9	10
⑪	12	⑬	14	15	16	⑰	18	⑲	20
21	22	㉓	24	25	26	27	28	㉙	30
㉛	32	33	34	35	36	㊲	38	39	40
㊶	42	㊸	44	45	46	㊼	48	49	50
51	52	㊳	54	55	56	57	58	㊾	60
㊅	62	63	64	65	66	㊿	68	69	70
㉘	72	㋃	74	75	76	77	78	㋄	80
81	82	㋈	84	85	86	87	88	㋉	90
91	92	93	94	95	96	㋍	98	99	100

b) 3 of: 11 (11), 13 (31), 17 (71), 37 (73), 79 (97)
c) e.g. 3 is a factor of 27

Q7 113

Q8 There's just one: 2 is the only even prime.

Multiples, Factors and Prime Factors P.3-P.4

Q1 a) 12
b) 3
c) 1, 9
d) 1, 3, 9
e) P = 12, Q = 6

Q2 Any 5 of:
2 groups of 24, 3 groups of 16,
4 groups of 12, 6 groups of 8,
8 groups of 6, 12 groups of 4,
16 groups of 3, 24 groups of 2.

Q3 The Conversational French and Woodturning classes both have a prime number of pupils and so cannot be divided into equal groups.

Q4 a) 1, 8, 27, 64, 125
b) 8, 64
c) 27
d) 8, 64
e) 125

Q5 a) 2×3^2
b) $2^2 \times 5 \times 7$
c) 47

Q6 a) 2, 3, 5, 7, 11
b) 28
c) $2^2 \times 7$

Q7 a) 1, 3, 5, 7, 9
b) 25
c) 5^2

Q8 a) 495
b) $3 \times 5 \times 11$

Q9 a) 1, 4, 9, 16, 25, 36, 49, 64, 81, 100
b) 4, 16, 36, 64, 100
c) 9, 36, 81
d) 1, 64
e) Total = 385 = $5 \times 7 \times 11$

Q10 a) $50 \times 25 \times 16 = 20,000$ cm^3
b) $2^5 \times 5^4$
c) 200. It is not enough to divide the large volume by the smaller volume as the shapes of the blocks are important too. It is possible to fit $16 \div 4 = 4$ small blocks across the width, $50 \div 5 = 10$ small blocks along the length and $25 \div 5 = 5$ small blocks down the height of the large block. This enables Gordon to fit $4 \times 10 \times 5 = 200$ small blocks into the big block.

Q11 a) 680
b) $2^2 \times 5 \times 17$
c) $2 \times 5 \times 17$
d) 5×17

Q12 42

LCM and HCF P5

Q1 a) 6, 12, 18, 24, 30, 36, 42, 48, 54, 60
b) 5, 10, 15, 20, 25, 30, 35, 40, 45, 50
c) 30

Q2 a) 1, 2, 3, 5, 6, 10, 15, 30
b) 1, 2, 3, 4, 6, 8, 12, 16, 24, 48
c) 6

Q3 a) 20
b) 10
c) 2
d) 15
e) 15
f) 5
g) 32
h) 16
i) 16

Q4 a) 120
b) 120
c) 120
d) 45
e) 90
f) 180
g) 64
h) 192
i) 192

Q5 a) 7th June
b) 16th June
c) Sunday (1st July)
d) Lars

Fractions P6-P8

Q1 a) $\frac{1}{64}$
b) $\frac{1}{9}$
c) $\frac{1}{18}$
d) $3\frac{29}{32}$
e) $5\frac{5}{32}$
f) $\frac{81}{100\,000}$

Q2 a) 1
b) 4
c) $\frac{1}{2}$
d) $\frac{2}{5}$
e) $\frac{10}{33}$
f) 1000

Q3 a) $\frac{1}{4}$
b) $\frac{5}{6}$
c) $\frac{1}{2}$
d) $4\frac{3}{8}$

Answers: P.6 — P.12

e) $5\frac{3}{8}$

f) 1

Q4 $3\frac{7}{15}$, so the bowl will be big enough.

Q5 a) 0

b) $\frac{1}{2}$

c) $-\frac{1}{6}$

d) $1\frac{7}{8}$

e) $-3\frac{1}{8}$

f) $\frac{4}{5}$

Q6 a) $\frac{3}{4}$

b) $\frac{5}{12}$

c) $\frac{7}{15}$

d) $4\frac{3}{4}$

e) 4

f) $1\frac{1}{5}$

g) $\frac{5}{8}$

h) $-\frac{1}{24}$

i) $4\frac{3}{5}$

j) $1\frac{1}{30}$

k) 1

l) $\frac{44}{75}$

Q7 a) 1/12

b) 1/4

c) 2/3

Q8 a) 3/4 of the programme

b) 5/8 of the programme

c) 1/8 of the programme

Q9 3/5 of the kitchen staff are girls.
2/5 of the employees are boys.

Q10 7/30 of those asked had no opinion.

Q11 a) 12/30 = 2/5

b) 6 days

Q12 a) Each box will hold 16 sandwiches.
So 5 boxes will be needed for 80
sandwiches.

b) 25 inches tall

Q13 a) $\frac{1}{18}$

b) $\frac{1}{4}$

Q14 a) 48 km²

b) $\frac{5}{8}$

Q15 a) 8 people

b) $\frac{7}{20}$

c) $\frac{1}{4}$

d) 57 people

e) 65 people

Q16 After the 1st bounce the ball reaches
4 m, after the 2nd $2\frac{2}{3}$ m, after the 3rd
$1\frac{7}{9}$ m.

Q17 a) 100 g flour

b) 350 g

c) $\frac{2}{7}$

d) 300 g

Q18 £31.06

Fractions, Decimals and Percentages P.9-P.10

Q1 a) 25%

b) 50%

c) 75%

d) 10%

e) 41.52%

f) 84.06%

g) 39.62%

h) 28.28%

Q2 a) 0.5

b) 0.12

c) 0.4

d) 0.34

e) 0.602

f) 0.549

g) 0.431

h) 0.788

Q3 a) 50%

b) 25%

c) 12.5%

d) 75%

e) 4%

f) 66.7%

g) 26.7%

h) 28.6%

Q4 a) 1/4

b) 3/5

c) 9/20

d) 3/10

e) 41/500

f) 62/125

g) 443/500

h) 81/250

Q5 85%

Q6 Grade C

Q7 a) 0.3   e) 1.75

b) 0.37   f) 0.125

c) 0.4   g) 0.6

d) 0.375   h) 0.05

Q8

Fraction	Decimal
1/2	0.5
1/5	0.2
1/8	0.125
8/5	1.6
4/16	0.25
7/2	3.5
x/10	0.x
x/100	0.0x
3/20	0.15
9/20	0.45

Q9 a) $0.8\dot{3}$ e) $0.\overline{90}$

b) $0.\dot{7}$ f) $0.\overline{460317}$

c) $0.\overline{63}$ g) $0.4\overline{78}$

d) $0.\overline{47}$ h) $0.5\overline{891}$

Q10 a) $\frac{3}{5}$ e) $\frac{1}{3}$

b) $\frac{3}{4}$ f) $\frac{2}{3}$

c) $\frac{19}{20}$ g) $\frac{1}{9}$

d) $\frac{16}{125}$ h) $\frac{16}{99}$

Q11 a) $\frac{2}{9}$ e) $\frac{4}{33}$

b) $\frac{4}{9}$ f) $\frac{545}{999}$

c) $\frac{8}{9}$ g) $\frac{251}{333}$

d) $\frac{80}{99}$ h) $\frac{52}{333}$

Percentages P.11-P.12

Q1 a) £1.28

b) 629 kg

c) 16 mins

Q2 a) £24

b) £21

c) £4

Q3 a) £4275   b) £6840

Q4 £358.80

Q5 £244.40

Q6 23 028

Q7 Car 1 costs £8495 – (0.15 × £8495)
= £8495 – £1274.25 = £7220.75.
Car 2 costs £8195 – (0.12 × £8195)
= £8195 – £983.40 = £7211.60.
So car 2 is the cheapest.

Q8 a) 67.7%

b) 93.5%

c) 38.1%

Q9 500%

Q10 31%

Q11 13%

Q12 £80

Q13 a) 300

b) 4 whole years

GCSE
Mathematics
Exam Board: WJEC

The Answer Book
Higher Level

Includes **Free** Online Edition

Contents

How to get your free Online Edition

This book includes a **free** Online Edition you can read on
your computer or tablet. To access it, just go to
cgpbooks.co.uk/extras and enter this code...

3097 2576 1286 6813

By the way, this code only works for one person. If somebody else has used
this book before you, they might have already claimed the Online Edition.

Published by CGP

ISBN: 978 1 84762 511 3

Groovy website: www.cgpbooks.co.uk
Printed by Elanders Ltd, Newcastle upon Tyne.
Jolly bits of clipart from CorelDRAW®
Text, design, layout and original illustrations © Richard Parsons. 2013

Answers: P.12 — P.19

Q14 a) £236.25
  b) £1000 × 1.07³ – £1000 = £225.04
  c) £1000 × 1.07875³ – £1000 = £255.34

Compound Growth and Decay P.13

Q1 a) £473.47   **c)** £909.12
  b) £612.52   **d)** £1081.90

Q2 a) 280
  b) 3035
  c) 27 hours

Q3 a) 8.214 kg   **c)** 7.272 kg
  b) 7.497 kg   **d)** 3.836 kg

Q4 a) £1920.80   **c)** £434.06
  b) £27 671.04   **d)** £34 974.86

Q5 Second option by £2.20

Ratios P.14-P.15

Q1 a) 3:4   **d)** 9:16
  b) 1:4   **e)** 7:2
  c) 1:2   **f)** 9:1

Q2 a) 6 cm   **d)** 1.5 cm
  b) 11 cm   **e)** 2.75 cm
  c) 30.4 m   **f)** 7.6 m

Q3 a) £8, £12
  b) 80 m, 70 m
  c) 100 g, 200 g, 200 g
  d) 1hr 20 m, 2 hr 40 m, 4 hrs

Q4 John 4, Peter 12

Q5 400 ml, 600 ml, 1000 ml

Q6 30

Q7 Jane £40, Holly £48, Rosemary £12

Q8 Paul — £16

Q9 a) 250/500 = 1/2
  b) 150/500 = 3/10

Q10 a) 245 girls
  b) 210 boys

Q11 a) 39
  b) 140

Q12 a) 1:300
  b) 6 m
  c) 3.3 cm

Q13 a) 15 kg
  b) 30 kg
  c) 8 kg cement, 24 kg sand and 48 kg gravel.

Q14 a) 30 fine
  b) 15 not fine
  c) 30/45 = 2/3

Q15 a) 45 Salt & Vinegar
  b) 90 bags sold altogether

Rounding Numbers P.16

Q1 a) 62.2
  b) 62.19
  c) 62.194
  d) 19.62433
  e) 6.300
  f) 3.142

Q2 a) 1330
  b) 1330
  c) 1329.6
  d) 100
  e) 0.02
  f) 0.02469

Q3 a) 457.0
  b) 456.99
  c) 456.987
  d) 457
  e) 460
  f) 500

Q4 2.83

Q5 a) £1100   **d)** £3
  b) £88   **e)** £376
  c) £300   **f)** £44

Q6 23 kg

Q7 £5.07

Q8 235 miles

Estimating P.17

Q1 Mark's tank is approximately 4500 cm³, so it won't be big enough.

Q2 a) 6500 × 2 = 13 000
  b) 8000 × 1.5 = 12 000
  c) 40 × 1.5 × 5 = 300
  d) 45 ÷ 9 = 5
  e) 35 000 ÷ 7000 = 5
  f) $\frac{55 \times 20}{10} = 55 \times 2 = 110$
  g) 7000 × 2 = 14 000
  h) 100 × 2.5 × 2 = 500
  i) 20 × 20 × 20 = 8000
  j) 8000 ÷ 80 = 100
  k) 62 000 ÷ 1000 = 62
  l) 3 ÷ 3 = 1

Q3 Approximately 15 000 – (1500 + 2500 + 1500 + 1500 + 3000) = 5000

Q4 a) $\frac{150 + 50}{150 - 50} = \frac{200}{100} = 2$
  b) $\frac{20 \times 10}{\sqrt{400}} = \frac{200}{20} = 10$
  c) $\frac{2000 \times 4}{20 \times 5} = \frac{8000}{100} = 80$
  d) $\frac{10^2 \div 10}{4 \times 5} = \frac{10}{20} = 0.5$

Q5 a) 2 × (3 × 3) + 2 × (2 × 3.5) = 36 m²
  b) 3 tins

Q6 a) 6.9 (accept 6.8)
  b) 10.9 (accept 10.8)
  c) 9.2 (accept 9.1)

d) 4.1 (accept 4.2)
e) 9.9 (accept 9.8)
f) 5.8 (accept 5.9)

Bounds P.18-P.19

Q1 a) 64.785 kg
  b) 64.775 kg

Q2 a) 1.75 m
  b) 1.85 × 0.75 = 1.3875 m²

Q3 a) 2.525 l
  b) 2.475 l

Q4 a) 95 g
  b) Upper bound = 97.5 g, lower bound = 92.5 g.
  c) No, since the lower bound for the electronic scales is 97.5 g, which is greater than the upper bound for the scales in part **a)**.

Q5 a) Upper bound = 13.5, lower bound = 12.5
  b) Upper bound = 12.55, lower bound = 12.45
  c) To calculate the upper bound for C multiply the upper bound for A by the upper bound for B; 13.5×12.55 = 169.425
  To calculate the lower bound for C multiply the lower bound for A by the lower bound for B; 12.5×12.45 = 155.625

Q6 a) Upper bound = 5 minutes 32.5 seconds, lower bound = 5 minutes 27.5 seconds.
  b) The lower bound for Jimmy's time is 5 minutes 25 seconds, which is lower than the lower bound for Douglas' time (5 minutes 25.5 seconds).

Q7 a) Upper bound = 945, lower bound = 935.
  b) Upper bound = 5.565, lower bound = 5.555.
  c) To find the upper bound for R, divide the upper bound for S by the lower bound for T; 945 ÷ 5.555 = 170.117...
  To find the lower bound for R, divide the lower bound for S by the upper bound for T; 935÷5.565 = 168.014...
  d) 940÷5.56 = 170 (to 2 s.f. — the upper and lower bounds both round to 170 to 2 s.f., but give different answers to 3 s.f.).

Q8 At least 18.2 m²

Q9 The upper bound for the distance is 127.5 km. The lower bound for the time is 1 hour and 45 minutes = 1.75 hours. The maximum value of the average speed is 127.5÷1.75 = 72.857... km/hour.

Q10 a) Perimeter = 2(12 + 4) = 32 cm.
Maximum possible error
= 4 × 0.1 cm = 0.4 cm.
b) Maximum possible error in P is
2(x + y).

Standard Form P.20

Q1 a) 35.6 **b)** 3560
c) 0.356 **d)** 35600
e) 8.2 **f)** 0.00082
g) 0.82 **h)** 0.0082
i) 1570 **j)** 0.157
k) 157000 **l)** 15.7

Q2 a) 2.56×10^0 **b)** 2.56×10
c) 2.56×10^{-1} **d)** 2.56×10^4
e) 9.52×10 **f)** 9.52×10^{-2}
g) 9.52×10^4 **h)** 9.52×10^{-4}
i) 4.2×10^3 **j)** 4.2×10^{-3}
k) 4.2×10 **l)** 4.2×10^2

Q3 a) 6×10^9 **b)** 1.89×10^7
c) 4×10^4 **d)** 2×10^2
e) 5.6×10^{16} **f)** 3.99×10^4
g) 4.3473×10^6 **h)** 1.748×10^4

Q4 a) 2.4×10^{10}
b) 1.6×10^6
c) 1.8×10^5

Q5 1.04×10^{13} is greater by 5.78×10^{12}

Q6 1.3×10^{-9} is smaller by 3.07×10^{-8}

Q7 7×10^6

Q8 6.38×10^8 cm

Q9 3.322×10^{-27} kg

Q10 a) 1.8922×10^{16} m
b) 4.7305×10^{15} m

Section Two — Algebra
Sequences P.21-P.22

Q1 a) 9, 11, 13, add 2 each time
b) 32, 64, 128, multiply by 2 each time
c) 30000, 300000, 3000000, multiply by 10 each time
d) 19, 23, 27, add 4 each time
e) -6, -11, -16, take 5 off each time

Q2 a) 4, 7, 10, 13, 16
b) 3, 8, 13, 18, 23
c) 1, 4, 9, 16, 25
d) -2, 1, 6, 13, 22

Q3 a) $2n$
b) $2n - 1$
c) $5n$
d) $3n + 2$

Q4 a) 19, 22, 25, $3n + 4$
b) 32, 37, 42, $5n + 7$
c) 46, 56, 66, $10n - 4$
d) 82, 89, 96, $7n + 47$

Q5 a) $16\frac{7}{8}$, $16\frac{9}{16}$, $16\frac{23}{32}$, $16\frac{41}{64}$
b) The 10th term will be the mean of the 8th and 9th.

Q6 a) The groups have 3, 8 and 15 triangles.
b) 24, 35, 48
c) $(n + 1)^2 - 1$ or $n^2 + 2n$

Q7 a) 23, 30, 38, $\frac{1}{2}(n^2 + 3n + 6)$
b) 30, 41, 54, $n^2 + 5$
c) 45, 64, 87, $2n^2 - 3n + 10$
d) 52, 69, 89, $\frac{1}{2}(3n^2 + n + 24)$

Q8 a) $\frac{(2n + 1)^2 + 1}{2}$
b) $\frac{(2n + 1)^2 - 1}{2}$
c) $(2n + 1)^2$

Powers and Roots P.23-P.24

Q1 a) 16
b) 1000
c) $3 \times 3 \times 3 \times 3 \times 3 = 243$
d) $4 \times 4 \times 4 \times 4 \times 4 \times 4 = 4096$
e) $1 \times 1 \times 1 \times 1 \times 1 \times 1 \times 1 \times 1 \times 1 = 1$
f) $5 \times 5 \times 5 \times 5 \times 5 \times 5 = 15\ 625$

Q2 a) 2^8 (or 256)
b) 12^5 (or 248 832)
c) x^5
d) m^3
e) y^4
f) z^6

Q3 b) 10^7
c) 10^6
d) 10^8
e) Simply add the powers.

Q4 b) 2^3
c) 4^2
d) 8^3
e) Simply subtract the powers.

Q5 a) true **b)** true
c) false **d)** false
e) true **f)** false
g) false **h)** true
i) false **j)** true
k) true **l)** false

Q6 a) 3^{-3} **d)** 3^{-12}
b) 4^{25} **e)** 4^6
c) 10^{-13} **f)** 5^3

Q7 a) 275 **b)** 0.123
c) 53 400 **d)** 6.40×10^{-5}
e) 2.37 **f)** 2.31
g) 10.4 **h)** 0.843
i) 2.25 **j)** 2.18
k) 0.244 **l)** 0.965

Q8 a) 8.76 **b)** 4.17
c) 19.4 **d)** 219
e) 108 **f)** 91.9
g) 13.6 **h)** 17.8
i) 5.06

Q9 a) 0.008 **b)** 0.25
c) 1.53×10^{-5} **d)** 0.667
e) 2.24 **f)** 1.82
g) 1.55 **h)** 2.60
i) 0.512 **j)** 1.21
k) 0.0352 **l)** 7.28

Q10 a) 1.49 **b)** 20.1
c) 2.50 **d)** 6.55
e) 1.08 **f)** 8.78
g) 0.707 **h)** −0.380

Q11 a) 9.14 **b)** 1.50
c) 0.406 **d)** 476
e) 0.0146 **f)** 1.22
g) 84.5 **h)** 0.496
i) 165 **j)** 8.47

Algebra Basics P.25

Q1 a) -27°C **d)** +18°C
b) -22°C **e)** +15°C
c) +12°C **f)** -12°C

Q2 Expression **b)** is larger by 1.

Q3 a) $-4x$ **b)** $18y$

Q4 a) $-1000, -10$ **c)** 144, 16
b) $-96, -6$ **d)** 0, 0

Q5 -4

Q6 a) $-6xy$ **g)** $\frac{-5x}{y}$
b) $-16ab$ **h)** 3
c) $8x^2$ **i)** -4
d) $-16p^2$ **j)** -10
e) $\frac{10x}{y}$ **k)** $4x$
f) $\frac{-10x}{y}$ **l)** $-8y$

Q7 a) $15x^2 - x$
b) $13x^2 - 5x$
c) $-7x^2 + 12x + 12$
d) $30abc + 12ab + 4b$
e) $18pq + 8p$
f) $17ab - 17a + b$
g) $4pq - 5p - 9q$
h) $16x^2 - 4y^2$
i) $abc + 10ab - 11cd$
j) $-2x^2 + y^2 - z^2 + 6xy$

Multiplying Out Brackets P.26

Q1 a) $4x + 4y - 4z$
b) $x^2 + 5x$
c) $-3x + 6$
d) $9a + 9b$
e) $-a + 4b$
f) $2x - 6$
g) $4e^2 - 2f^2 + 10ef$
h) $16m - 8n$

i) $6x^2 + 2x$

j) $-2ab + 11$

k) $-2x^2 - xz - 2yz$

l) $3x - 6y - 5$

m) $-3a - 4b$

n) $14pqr + 8pq + 35qr$

o) $x^3 + x^2$

p) $4x^3 + 8x^2 + 4x$

q) $8a^2b + 24ab + 8ab^2$

r) $7p^2q + 7pq^2 - 7q$

s) $16x - 8y$

Q2 **a)** $x^2 - 2x - 3$

b) $x^2 + 2x - 15$

c) $x^2 + 13x + 30$

d) $x^2 - 7x + 10$

e) $x^2 - 5x - 14$

f) $28 - 11x + x^2$

g) $6x - 2 + 9x^2 - 3x = 9x^2 + 3x - 2$

h) $6x^2 - 12x + 4x - 8 = 6x^2 - 8x - 8$

i) $4x^2 + x - 12x - 3 = 4x^2 - 11x - 3$

j) $4x^2 - 8xy + 2xy - 4y^2$
$= 4x^2 - 4y^2 - 6xy$

k) $12x^2 - 8xy + 24xy - 16y^2$
$= 12x^2 - 16y^2 + 16xy$

l) $9x^2 + 4y^2 + 12xy$

Q3 $15x^2 + 10x - 6x - 4 = 15x^2 + 4x - 4$

Q4 $4x^2 - 4x + 1$

Q5 **a)** $(4x + 6)$ m

b) $(-3x^2 + 17x - 10)$ m^2

Q6 **a)** $(8x + 20)$ cm

b) $40x$ cm^2

c) $40x - 12x = 28x$ cm^2

Q7 **a)** Perimeter — $3x + 29$ cm
Area — $\frac{7x + 126}{2}$ cm^2

b) Perimeter — $(8x + 4)$ cm
Area — $(3x^2 + 14x - 24)$ cm^2

c) Perimeter — $(16x - 4)$ cm
Area — $(16x^2 - 8x + 1)$ cm^2

d) Perimeter — $(10x + 4)$ cm
Area — $(6x^2 - 5x - 6)$ cm^2

Factorising P.27

Q1 **a)** $a^2(b + c)$

b) $a^2(5 + 13b)$

c) $a^2(2b + 3c)$

d) $a^2(a + y)$

e) $a^2(2x + 3y + 4z)$

f) $a^2(b^2 + ac^2)$

Q2 **a)** $x(x - 5)$

b) $2(x + 3)$

c) $3x(x + 4)$

d) $2x(2x - 3)$

e) $3xy(1 + 4x)$

f) $3(3x + 5)$

g) $5x(3xy - 5)$

h) $4pq(q - 5 + 2p)$

i) $2x(5x^3 + 3)$

j) $5x^2(3x - 4)$

k) $7x(3x + 2)$

l) $5xy(z + 4u)$

Q3 **a)** $4xyz(1 + 2) = 12xyz$

b) $4xyz(2 + 3) = 20xyz$

c) $8xyz(1 + 2x)$

d) $4xyz^2(5xy + 4)$

Q4 **a)** $(x + 3)(x - 3)$

b) $(y + 4)(y - 4)$

c) $(5 + z)(5 - z)$

d) $(6 + a)(6 - a)$

e) $(2x + 3)(2x - 3)$

f) $(3y + 2)(3y - 2)$

g) $(5 + 4z)(5 - 4z)$

h) $(1 + 6a)(1 - 6a)$

i) $(x^2 + 6)(x^2 - 6)$

j) $(x^2 + y^2)(x^2 - y^2)$

k) $(1 + ab)(1 - ab)$

l) $(10x + 12y)(10x - 12y)$

Q5 **a)** $(x + 2)(x - 2)$

b) $(12 + y^2)(12 - y^2)$

c) $(1 + 3xy)(1 - 3xy)$

d) $(7x^2y^2 + 1)(7x^2y^2 - 1)$

Q6 **a)** $16a^2b^2(4b - a)$

b) $q(p + r - pqr)$

c) $3(m^2 - 8)$

d) $b^2(b^2 - ab + c)$

e) $(a^2 - 13)(a^2 + 13)$

f) $3ab(3b - c)$

g) $(9 - z)(9 + z)$

h) $(6m - 5n)(6m + 5n)$

i) $mn(m + 3 - 2n^2)$

j) $(11p - 3q)(11p + 3q)$

k) $12(12x^2 - 9y^2 - 5z^2)$

l) $(8ab - 7cd)(8ab + 7cd)$

Manipulating Surds P.28

Q1 **a)** $\sqrt{15}$

b) 2

c) x

d) x

e) 8

f) $\sqrt{5}$

Q2 3π cm^2

Q3 **a)** 1 **e)** $3\sqrt{5}$

b) $5\sqrt{3}$ **f)** $5\sqrt{2}$

c) $2\sqrt{2}$ **g)** $\sqrt{2}$

d) $7 + 4\sqrt{3}$ **h)** $3(\sqrt{2} - 1)$

Q4 **a)** $(1 + \sqrt{5})(1 - \sqrt{5}) = -4$, rational

b) $\frac{1 + \sqrt{5}}{1 - \sqrt{5}} = -\frac{1}{2}(3 + \sqrt{5})$, irrational

Q5 **a)** $(x + y)(x - y) = -1$, rational

b) $\frac{x + y}{x - y} = -3 - 2\sqrt{2}$, irrational

Q6 **a)** $\frac{\sqrt{2}}{2}$ **e)** $\sqrt{2} - 1$

b) $\frac{\sqrt{2}}{2}$ **f)** $3 - \sqrt{3}$

c) $\frac{\sqrt{10}a}{10}$ **g)** $\frac{2[\sqrt{6} - 1]}{5}$

d) $\frac{\sqrt{xy}}{y}$ **h)** $\frac{3 + \sqrt{5}}{2}$

Solving Equations P.29-P.30

Q1 1

Q2 **a)** $x = \pm 3$ **d)** $x = \pm 3$

b) $x = \pm 6$ **e)** $x = \pm 1$

c) $x = \pm 3$

Q3 **a)** $x = 5$ **d)** $x = -6$

b) $x = 4$ **e)** $x = 5$

c) $x = 10$ **f)** $x = 9$

Q4 **a)** $x = 5$ **e)** $x = 6$

b) $x = 2$ **f)** $x = 5$

c) $x = 8$ **g)** $x = \pm 2$

d) $x = 17$

Q5 **a)** 15.5 cm   **b)** 37.2 cm

Q6 £15.50

Q7 **a)** $x = 9$ **g)** $x = 15$

b) $x = 2$ **h)** $x = 110$

c) $x = 3$ **i)** $x = \pm 6$

d) $x = 3$ **j)** $x = 66$

e) $x = 4$ **k)** $x = 700$

f) $x = -1$ **l)** $x = 7\frac{1}{2}$

Q8 **a)** Joan — £x
Kate — £$2x$
Linda — £$(x - 232)$

b) $4x = 2632$
$x = 658$

c) Kate — £1316
Linda — £426

Q9 **a)** $2x + 32$ cm

b) $12x$ cm^2

c) $x = 3.2$

Q10 **a)** $x = 0.75$ **d)** $x = -1$

b) $x = -1$ **e)** $x = 4$

c) $x = -6$ **f)** $x = 13$

Q11 $x = 8$

Q12 $x = 1$

Q13 8 yrs

Q14 39, 35, 8

Q15 **a)** $y = 22$ **f)** $x = 7$

b) $x = 8$ **g)** $x = \pm 3$

c) $z = -5$ **h)** $x = \pm 4$

d) $x = 19$ **i)** $x = \pm 7$

e) $x = 23$

Q16 $x = 1\frac{1}{2}$

Q17 **a)** $x = 5$ **b)** $x = 9$

Q18 $x = 1\frac{1}{2}$ AB = 5 cm
AC = $5\frac{1}{2}$ cm
BC = $7\frac{1}{2}$ cm

Answers: P.31 — P.34

Rearranging Formulas P.31-P.32

Q1 **a)** $h = \frac{10 - g}{4}$

b) $c = 2d - 4$

c) $k = 3 + \frac{j}{2}$

d) $b = \frac{3a}{2}$

e) $g = \frac{8f}{3}$

f) $x = 2(y + 3)$

g) $t = 6(s - 10)$

h) $q = \pm \frac{\sqrt{p}}{2}$

Q2 **a)** $c = \frac{w - 500m}{50}$

b) 132

Q3 **a) i)** £38.00   **ii)** £48.00
b) $c = 28 + 0.25n$
c) $n = 4(c - 28)$
d) i) 24 miles **ii)** 88 miles
     iii) 114 miles

Q4 **a)** $x = \pm \sqrt{y + 2}$

b) $x = y^2 - 3$

c) $s = \pm 2\sqrt{r}$

d) $g = 3f - 10$

e) $z = 5 - 2w$

f) $x = \pm \sqrt{\frac{3v}{h}}$

g) $a = \frac{v^2 - u^2}{2s}$

h) $u = \pm \sqrt{v^2 - 2as}$

i) $g = \frac{4\pi^2 l}{t^2}$

Q5 **a)** £Jx
b) $P = T - Jx$
c) $J = \frac{T - P}{x}$
d) £16

Q6 **a) i)** £2.04   **ii)** £3.48
b) $C = (12x + 60)$ pence
c) $x = \frac{C - 60}{12}$
d) i) 36   **ii)** 48   **iii)** 96

Q7 **a)** $x = \frac{z}{y + 2}$

b) $x = \frac{b}{a - 3}$

c) $x = \frac{y}{4 - z}$

d) $x = \frac{3z + y}{y + 5}$

e) $x = \frac{-2}{y - z}$ or $\frac{2}{z - y}$

f) $x = \frac{2y + 3z}{2 - z}$

g) $x = \frac{-y - wz}{yz - 1}$ or $\frac{y + wz}{1 - yz}$

h) $x = \frac{-z}{4}$

Q8 **a)** $p = \frac{4r - 2q}{q - 3}$

b) $g = \frac{5 - 2e}{f + 2}$

c) $b = \frac{3c + 2a}{a - c}$

d) $q = \pm \sqrt{\frac{4}{p - r}} = \pm \frac{2}{\sqrt{p - r}}$

e) $a = \frac{2c + 4b}{4 + c - d}$

f) $x = \pm \sqrt{\frac{-3y}{2}}$

g) $k = \pm \sqrt{\frac{14}{h - 1}}$

h) $x = \left(\frac{4 - y}{2 - z}\right)^2$

i) $a = \frac{b^2}{3 + b}$

j) $m = -7n$

k) $e = \frac{d}{50}$

l) $y = \frac{x}{3x + 2}$

Q9 **a)** $y = \frac{x}{x - 1}$

b) $y = \frac{-3 - 2x}{x - 1}$ or $\frac{2x + 3}{1 - x}$

c) $y = \pm \sqrt{\frac{x + 1}{2x - 1}}$

d) $y = \pm \sqrt{\frac{1 + 2x}{3x - 2}}$

Factorising Quadratics P.33

Q1 **a)** $(x + 5)(x - 2)$
     $x = -5, x = 2$
b) $(x - 3)(x - 2)$
     $x = 3, x = 2$
c) $(x - 1)^2$
     $x = 1$
d) $(x - 3)(x - 1)$
     $x = 3, x = 1$
e) $(x - 5)(x + 4)$
     $x = 5, x = -4$
f) $(x + 1)(2x - 5)$
     $x = -1, x = \frac{5}{2}$
g) $(3x + 7)(x - 1)$
     $x = -\frac{7}{3}, x = 1$
h) $(x + 7)^2$
     $x = -7$
i) $(x - 5)(2x + 3)$
     $x = 5, x = -\frac{3}{2}$

Q2 **a)** $(x + 8)(x - 2)$
     $x = -8, x = 2$
b) $(x + 9)(x - 4)$
     $x = -9, x = 4$
c) $(x + 9)(x - 5)$
     $x = -9, x = 5$
d) $x(x - 5)$
     $x = 0, x = 5$
e) $x(x - 11)$
     $x = 0, x = 11$
f) $(x - 7)(x + 3)$
     $x = 7, x = -3$
g) $(x - 30)(x + 10)$
     $x = 30, x = -10$

h) $(x - 24)(x - 2)$
     $x = 24, x = 2$
i) $(x - 9)(x - 4)$
     $x = 9, x = 4$
j) $(x + 7)(x - 2)$
     $x = -7, x = 2$
k) $(x + 7)(x - 3)$
     $x = -7, x = 3$
l) $(x - 5)(x + 2)$
     $x = 5, x = -2$
m) $(x - 6)(x + 3)$
     $x = 6, x = -3$
n) $(x - 9)(x + 7)$
     $x = 9, x = -7$
o) $(x + 4)(x - 3)$
     $x = -4, x = 3$

Q3 $x = \frac{1}{2}$, $x = -\frac{1}{2}$

Q4 $x = 4$

Q5 **a)** $(x^2 - x)$ m²
b) $x = 3$

Q6 **a)** $x(x + 1)$ cm²
b) $x = 3$

Q7 **a)** x^2 m²
b) $12x$ m²
c) $x^2 + 12x - 64 = 0$
     $x = 4$

The Quadratic Formula P.34-P.35

Q1 **a)** 1.87, 0.13
b) 2.39, 0.28
c) 1.60, - 3.60
d) 1.16, -3.16
e) 0.53, -4.53
f) -11.92, -15.08
g) -2.05, -4.62
h) 0.84, 0.03

Q2 **a)** -2, -6
b) 0.67, -0.5
c) 3, -2
d) 2, 1
e) 3, 0.75
f) 3, 0
g) 0.67
h) 0, -2.67
i) 4, -0.5
j) 4, -5
k) 1, -3
l) 5, -1.33
m) 1.5, -1
n) -2.5, 1
o) 0.5, 0.33
p) 1, -3
q) 2, -6
r) 2, -4

Q3 **a)** 0.30, -3.30
b) 3.65, -1.65
c) 0.62, -1.62
d) -0.55, -5.45
e) -0.44, -4.56

Answers: P.34 — P.39

f) 1.62, -0.62
g) 0.67, -4.00
h) -0.59, -3.41
i) 7.12, -1.12
j) 13.16, 0.84
k) 1.19, -4.19
l) 1.61, 0.53
m) 0.44, -3.44
n) 2.78, 0.72

Q4 a) 1.7, -4.7
b) -0.27, -3.73
c) 1.88, -0.88
d) 0.12, -4.12
e) 4.83, -0.83
f) 1.62, -0.62
g) 1.12, -1.79
h) -0.21, -4.79
i) 2.69, -0.19
j) 2.78, 0.72
k) 1, 0
l) 1.5, 0.50

Q5 $x^2 - 3.6x + 3.24 = 0$
$x = 1.8$

Q6 a) $x^2 + 2.5x - 144.29 = 0$
$x = 10.83$
b) 48.3 cm

Algebraic Fractions P36

Q1 a) $\frac{3xy}{z}$ **c)** $\frac{1}{3xy^2z^3}$
b) $\frac{12b^2}{c}$ **d)** $\frac{q^3}{2r^3}$

Q2 a) $\frac{2}{xy}$ **d)** $\frac{90ac^4}{b}$
b) $\frac{3a^2b}{2}$ **e)** $\frac{3a^4c^3}{2bd}$
c) $\frac{8x^2z^2}{y}$ **f)** 1

Q3 a) $2x^2y$ **d)** $5x^3$
b) a **e)** $\frac{5a^3}{b}$
c) $2ef$ **f)** $\frac{2x}{y^2z}$

Q4 a) $\frac{3+y}{2x}$ **d)** $\frac{14x+y}{6}$
b) $\frac{1+y}{x}$ **e)** $\frac{7x}{6}$
c) $\frac{7x+6}{x}$ **f)** $\frac{37x}{42}$

Q5 a) $\frac{4x-5y}{3}$ **d)** $\frac{4x-y}{6}$
b) $\frac{4x-1}{y}$ **e)** $\frac{b(14-a)}{7a}$
c) $\frac{-1}{4x}$ **f)** $\frac{-p+5q}{10}$

Q6 a) $\frac{a^2}{b^2}$
b) $\frac{mn(pm+1)}{p^2}$
c) $\frac{2(a^2+b^2)}{a^2-b^2}$

Inequalities P37-P38

Q1 a) $9 \le x < 13$
b) $-4 \le x < 1$
c) $x \ge -4$
d) $x < 5$
e) $x > 25$
f) $-1 < x \le 3$
g) $0 < x \le 5$
h) $x < -2$

Q2
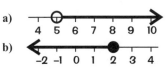
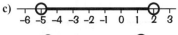
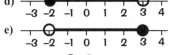

Q3 a) $x > 3$
b) $x < 4$
c) $x \le 5$
d) $x \le 6$
e) $x \ge 7.5$
f) $x < 4$
g) $x < 7$
h) $x < 4$
i) $x \ge 3$
j) $x > 11$
k) $x < 3$
l) $x \ge -\frac{1}{2}$
m) $x \le -2$
n) $x > 5$
o) $x < 15$
p) $x \ge -2$

Q4 Largest integer for x is 2.

Q5 $\frac{11-x}{2} < 5, x > 1$

Q6 $1130 \le 32x$
36 classrooms are needed.

Q7 50 guests (including bride and groom), $900 \ge 18x$

Q8 $x \ge 2$, $y > 1$, $x + y \le 5$

Q9
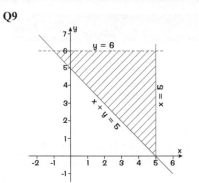

Q10
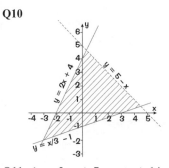

Q11 a) $x > 5$, $y \ge 7$, $x + y \ge 14$
b)
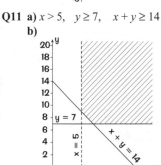

Trial and Improvement P39

Q1

Guess (x)	value of $x^3 + x$	Too large/small
2	$2^3 + 2 = 10$	Too small
3	$3^3 + 3 = 30$	Too large
2.6	$(2.6)^3 + 2.6 = 20.2$	Too small
2.7	$(2.7)^3 + 2.7 = 22.4$	Too small
2.8	$(2.8)^3 + 2.8 = 24.8$	Too large
2.75	$(2.75)^3 + 2.75 = 23.5$	Too small

So to 1 d.p. the solution is $x = 2.8$

Q2

Guess (x)	value of $x^3 + x^2 - 4x$	Too large/small
-3	$(-3)^3 + (-3)^2 - 4(-3) = -6$	Too small
-2	$(-2)^3 + (-2)^2 - 4(-2) = 4$	Too large
-2.1	$(-2.1)^3 + (-2.1)^2 - 4(-2.1) = 3.549$	Too large
-2.2	$(-2.2)^3 + (-2.2)^2 - 4(-2.2) = 2.99$	Too small
-2.15	$(-2.15)^3 + (-2.15)^2 - 4(-2.15) = 3.3$	Too large

So to 1 d.p. the solution is $x = -2.2$

SECTION TWO — ALGEBRA

Answers: P.39 — P.43

Guess (x)	value of $x^3 + x^2 - 4x$	Too large/small
-1	$-1 + 1 + 4 = 4$	Too large
0	$0 + 0 - 0 = 0$	Too small
-0.8	$(-0.8)^3 + (-0.8)^2 - 4(-0.8) = 3.328$	Too large
-0.7	$(-0.7)^3 + (-0.7)^2 - 4(-0.7) = 2.947$	Too small
-0.75	$(-0.75)^3 + (-0.75)^2 - 4(-0.75) = 3.141$	Too large

So to 1 d.p. the solution is $x = -0.7$

Guess (x)	value of $x^3 + x^2 - 4x$	Too large/small
1	$1 + 1 - 4 = -2$	Too small
2	$8 + 4 - 8 = 4$	Too large
1.9	$(1.9)^3 + (1.9)^2 - 4(1.9) = 2.869$	Too small
1.95	$(1.95)^3 + (1.95)^2 - 4(1.95) = 3.417$	Too large

So to 1 d.p. the solution is $x = 1.9$

Q3 Try different values of x to 1 d.p. between 3 and 4 to see which gives the highest value of V, e.g:

Guess (x)	value of $4x^3 - 80x^2 + 400x$
3	$108 - 720 + 1200 = 588$
4	$256 - 1280 + 1600 = 576$
3.5	$171.5 - 980 + 1400 = 591.5$
3.4	$157.216 - 924.8 + 1360 = 592.416$
3.3	$143.748 - 871.2 + 1320 = 592.548$
3.2	$131.072 - 819.2 + 1280 = 591.872$

So to 1 d.p. the solution is $x = 3.3$

Simultaneous Equations and Graphs P.40

Q1 **a)** $x = 3, y = 3$
  b) $x = 2, y = 5$
  c) $x = 1, y = 2$
  d) $x = 1, y = 2$
  e) $x = 1, y = 4$
  f) $x = 1, y = 2$
  g) $x = 2, y = 3$
  h) $x = 2, y = 3$
  i) $x = 5, y = 2$
  j) $x = 3, y = 4$

Q2 **a)** $x = 0, x = 1$
  b) $x = 2.7, x = -0.7$
  c) $x = 3.4, x = -2.4$
  d) $x = 1.6, x = -2.6$
  e) $x = 0.7$
  f) $x = 3.4, x = -2.4$
  g) $x = 1.6, x = -2.6$

Q3

x	-4	-3	-2	-1	0	1	2	3	4
$-\frac{1}{2}x^2$	-8	-4.5	-2	-0.5	0	-0.5	-2	-4.5	-8
$+5$	5	5	5	5	5	5	5	5	5
y	-3	0.5	3	4.5	5	4.5	3	0.5	-3

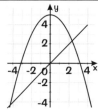

a) $x = 3.2, x = -3.2$
b) $x = 4, x = -4$
c) $x = 2.3, x = -4.3$

Simultaneous Equations P.41

Q1 **a)** $x = 1, y = 2$
  b) $x = 0, y = 3$
  c) $x = -1\frac{1}{2}, y = 4$

Q2 **a)** $6x + 5y = 430$
    $4x + 10y = 500$
  b) $x = 45, y = 32$

Q3 7 chickens
  4 cats

Q4 5 g (jellies are 4 g)

Q5 **a)** $3y + 2x = 18$
    $y + 3x = 6$ $x = 0, y = 6$
  b) $4y + 5x = 7$
    $2x - 3y = 12$ $x = 3, y = -2$
  c) $4x - 6y = 13$
    $x + y = 2$ $x = 2\frac{1}{2}, y = -\frac{1}{2}$

Q6 $5m + 2c = 344$
  $4m + 3c = 397$
  $m = 34p, c = 87p$

Q7 $x = 12, y = 2$

Direct and Inverse Proportion P.42

Q1 $y = 20$

Q2 $y = 184.8$

Q3 $y = 2$

Q4 $x = 2$

Q5

x	1	2	3	4	5	6
y	48	24	16	12	9.6	8

Q6

x	1	2	5	10
y	100	25	4	1

x	2	4	6	8
y	24	6	$2^2/_3$	1.5

Q7 4 kg

Q8 **a)** $r = 96$
  b) $s = 4$
  c) $r = 600$
  d) $s = -8$

Q9 9.5 N kg⁻¹

Proof P.43

Q1 $(n + 3)^2 - (3n + 5)$
  $= (n + 3)(n + 3) - (3n + 5)$
  $= n^2 + 6n + 9 - 3n - 5$
  $= n^2 + 3n + 2 + 2$
  $= (n + 1)(n + 2) + 2$

Q2 $(n - 3)^2 - (n - 5)$
  $= (n - 3)(n - 3) - (n - 5)$
  $= n^2 - 6n + 9 - n + 5$
  $= n^2 - 7n + 12 + 2$
  $= (n - 3)(n - 4) + 2$

Q3 $25 - \dfrac{(x - 8)^2}{4}$
  $= \dfrac{100 - (x - 8)^2}{4}$
  $= \dfrac{-x^2 + 16x + 36}{4}$
  $= \dfrac{(2 + x)(18 - x)}{4}$

Q4 $(2n + 1)^2 - (2n - 1)^2 - 10$
  $= (4n^2 + 4n + 1) - (4n^2 - 4n + 1) - 10$
  $= 8n - 10$
  Dividing this by 8 gives $n - \dfrac{5}{4}$
  (not a whole number), so the total is not divisible by 8.

Q5 $n + (n + 1) + (n + 2)$
  $= 3n + 3 = 3(n + 1)$
  Dividing this by 3 gives $n + 1$ (a whole number), so the total is divisible by 3.

Q6 $2a \times 2b = 4ab$, which must be even.

Q7 $2n + (2n + 2) + (2n + 4)$
  $= 6n + 6 = 6(n + 1)$
  Dividing this by 6 gives $n + 1$ (a whole number), so the total is a multiple of 6.

Q8 **a)** $(2n + 1) + (2n + 3)$
    $= 4n + 4 = 4(n + 1)$
    Dividing this by 4 gives $n + 1$
    (a whole number), so the total is a multiple of 4.
  b) $(2n + 1)^2 + (2n + 3)^2$
    $= 4n^2 + 4n + 1 + 4n^2 + 12n + 9$
    $= 8n^2 + 16n + 10$
    Dividing this by 4 gives
    $= 2n^2 + 4n + \dfrac{5}{2}$ (not a whole number), so the total is not divisible by 4.

Q9 2 is a prime number as it only divides by 1 and itself. 2 is even so Maisy is wrong.

Q10 **a)** 3 and 1 are both odd numbers but if you add them together you get 4, which is even so the statement is wrong.
  b) If n = 6, $n^2 = 36$ so the statement is wrong as 36 is divisible by 4 but 6 is not divisible by 4.

Q11 If $a = 1$ and $b = -1$, then $a^2 = 1$ and $b^2 = 1$. So, $a^2 = b^2$, but a does not equal b, so the statement is wrong.

Answers: P.44 — P.47

Section Three — Graphs
X and Y Coordinates P44-P45

Q1

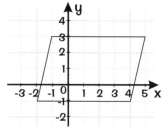

missing coordinate = (5,3)

Q2

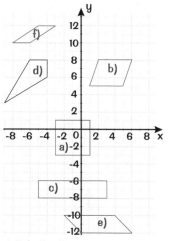

a) B is (1, -3)
b) C is (5, 5)
c) A is (-5, -8)
d) D is (-4, 6)
e) D is (0, -12)
f) C is (-3, 12)

Q3

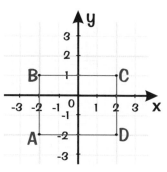

C = (2, 1), D = (2, -2)

Q4 **a)** (3,4)
b) (5.5,5)
c) (5.5,11)
d) (8.5,9)
e) (3,3.5)
f) (9.5,9.5)
g) (20,41.5)
h) (30.5,20.5)

Q5 (110,135)

Q6 **a)** (2,5.5)
b) (0.5,1.5)
c) (2,–2.5)
d) (1,–1)
e) (2,3)
f) (4,–0.5)
g) (–13,–12.5)
h) (–5,–7)

Straight-Line Graphs P46-P47

Q1 **a)** B   **f)** F
b) A   **g)** C
c) F   **h)** B
d) G   **i)** D
e) E   **j)** H

Q2

x	-4	-3	-2	-1	0	1	2	3	4
3x	-12	-9	-6	-3	0	3	6	9	12
-1	-1	-1	-1	-1	-1	-1	-1	-1	-1
y	-13	-10	-7	-4	-1	2	5	8	11

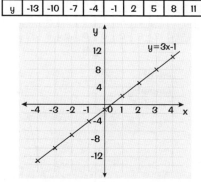

Q3

x	-6	-4	-2	0	2	4	6
1/2 x	-3	-2	-1	0	1	2	3
-3	-3	-3	-3	-3	-3	-3	-3
y	-6	-5	-4	-3	-2	-1	0

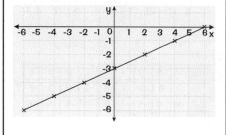

Q4

x	0	3	8
y	3	9	19

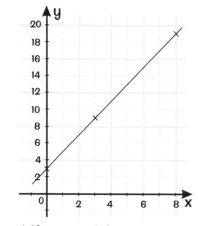

a) 13   **c)** 4
b) 7   **d)** 7

Q5

x	-8	-4	8
y	-5	-4	-1

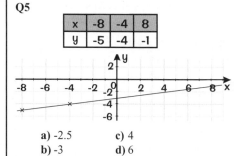

a) -2.5   **c)** 4
b) -3   **d)** 6

Q6

Number of Units used	0	100	200	300
Cost using method A	10	35	60	85
Cost using method B	40	45	50	55

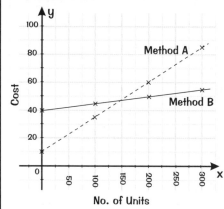

a) i) £27.50   **ii)** £43.50
b) Method A
c) 150 units

Answers: P.48 — P.53

Finding the Gradient P.48

Q1 a) $-\frac{1}{2}$ h) 1

     b) 3   i) -1

     c) $-\frac{1}{4}$ j) $\frac{1}{3}$

     d) -2   k) $-\frac{1}{2}$

     e) $-\frac{2}{3}$ l) 3

     f) $-\frac{8}{3}$

     g) 4

Q2 a) 2   d) -2

     b) $\frac{1}{2}$ e) $\frac{1}{2}$

     c) -1   f) $-\frac{3}{4}$

Q3 a) A and C.

     b) Gradient of D = $\frac{-1}{3}$

     c) $\frac{-1}{3}$

Q4 The gradient is -0.23 so it's a red run.

"y = mx + c" P.49

Q1 a) $m = 4$, (0, 3)

     b) $m = 3$, (0, -2)

     c) $m = 2$, (0, 1)

     d) $m = -3$, (0, 3)

     e) $m = 5$, (0, 0)

     f) $m = -2$, (0, 3)

     g) $m = -6$, (0, -4)

     h) $m = 1$, (0, 0)

     i) $m = -\frac{1}{2}$, (0, 3)

     j) $m = \frac{1}{4}$, (0, 2)

     k) $m = \frac{4}{3}$, (0, 2)

Q2 a) $y = \frac{7}{2}x - 1$ d) $y = \frac{1}{4}x - 3$

     b) $y = \frac{1}{2}x + 4$ e) $y = -\frac{1}{2}x$

     c) $y = -\frac{1}{5}x + 7$ f) $y = -2x - 6$

Q3 a) $y = x + 4$ c) $y = -x$

     b) $y = 3x + 2$ d) $y = -3x + 4$

Q4 a) $y = x$ c) $y = -3x + 3$

     b) $y = 3x$ d) $y = -2x - 4$

Q5 a) $x = 4$ c) $y = 7$

     b) $x = 8$ d) $y = 9$

Q6 (7, 20) and (5, 14)

Quadratic Graphs P.50

Q1

x	-4	-3	-2	-1	0	1	2	3	4
$y=2x^2$	32	18	8	2	0	2	8	18	32

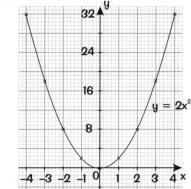

Q2

x	-4	-3	-2	-1	0	1	2	3	4
x^2	16	9	4	1	0	1	4	9	16
$y=x^2+x$	12	6	2	0	0	2	6	12	20

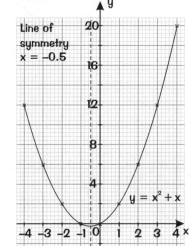

Q3 a)

x	-4	-3	-2	-1	0	1	2	3	4
3	3	3	3	3	3	3	3	3	3
$-x^2$	-16	-9	-4	-1	0	-1	-4	-9	-16
$y=3-x^2$	-13	-6	-1	2	3	2	-1	-6	-13

b)

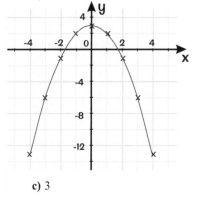

c) 3

Harder Graphs P.51-P.54

Q1 a) Cubic

     b) Straight Line

     c) Reciprocal

     d) Quadratic

     e) Cubic

     f) Reciprocal

     g) Exponential

     h) Quadratic

     i) Straight Line

     j) Cubic

     k) Cubic

     l) Quadratic

Q2 a) — vii)   i) — vi)

     b) — i)   j) — xii)

     c) — x)   k) — iv)

     d) — viii)   l) — xiii)

     e) — v)   m)— iii)

     f) — xiv)   n) — ii)

     g)— xi)   o) — ix)

     h) — xv)

Q3

x	-3	-2	-1	0	1	2	3
x^3	-27	-8	-1	0	1	8	27
+4	4	4	4	4	4	4	4
y	-23	-4	3	4	5	12	31

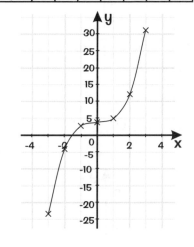

Answers: P.53 — P.56

Q4

x	-3	-2	-1	0	1	2	3
-x³	27	8	1	0	-1	-8	-27
-4	-4	-4	-4	-4	-4	-4	-4
y	23	4	-3	-4	-5	-12	-31

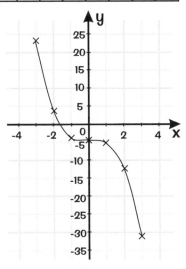

Q5 A(180,0)
B(90,1)   C(–90,–1)

Q6 D(270,0) F(0,1)
E(90,0)   G(–90,0)

Q7 A $y = \sin(x)$
B $y = \cos(x)$
C $y = \cos(x)$
D $y = \sin(x)$
E $y = \sin(x)$
F $y = \sin(x)$
G $y = \cos(x)$
H $y = \sin(x)$
I $y = \cos(x)$

Q8

x	0	90	180	270	360
y	2	1	0	1	2

Graph Transformations P.55-P.56

Q1 a) to d)

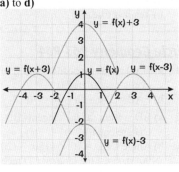

e) and f)

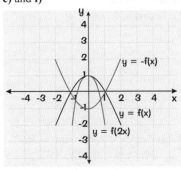

g) and h)

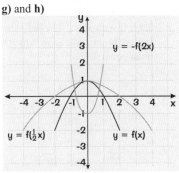

Q2 a) to d)

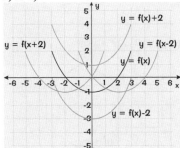

e) and f)

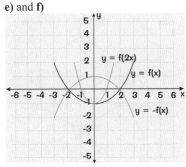

g) to i)

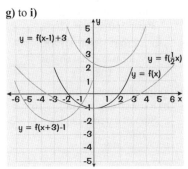

Q3 a) and b)

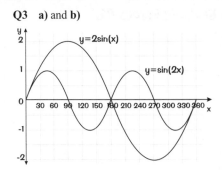

Q4 a) and b)

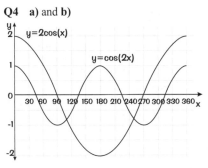

Q5 a) to d)

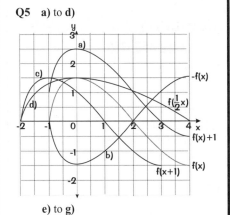

e) to g)

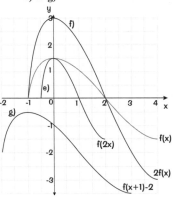

Answers: P.57 — P.63

Real-Life Graphs P.57

Q1 1 D
2 B
3 A
4 E
5 C

Q2

Number of Units used

a) Provider A: $P = 0.03N + 5$
Provider B: $P = 0.05N$
b) i) Provider A: £17; Provider B: £20
ii) Provider A: £26; Provider B: £35
c) 250 units

Section Four —
Geometry and Measure
Geometry P.58-P.59

Q1 **a)** $x = 47°$
b) $y = 154°$
c) $z = 22°$
d) $p = 35°, q = 45°$

Q2 **a)** $a = 146°$
b) $m = 131°, z = 48°$
c) $x = 68°, p = 112°$
d) $s = 20°, t = 90°$

Q3 **a)** $x = 96°, p = 38°$
b) $a = 108°, b = 23°, c = 95°$
c) $d = 120°, e = 60°, f = 60°, g = 120°$
d) $h = 155°, i = 77.5°, j = 102.5°,$
$k = 77.5°$

Q4 **a)** $b = 70°$ $c = 30°$
$d = 50°$ $e = 60°$
$f = 150°$
b) $g = 21°$ $h = 71°$
$i = 80°$ $j = 38°$
$k = 92°$
c) $l = 35°$ $m = 145°$
$n = 55°$ $p = 125°$

Q5 **a)** $x = 162°$ $y = 18°$
b) $x = 87°$ $y = 93°$
$z = 93°$
c) $a = 30°$ $2a = 60°$
$5a = 150°$ $4a = 120°$

Q6 **a)** $a = 141°,$ $b = 141°, c = 39°,$
$d = 141°,$ $e = 39°$
b) $a = 47°,$ $b = 47°,$ $c = 133°,$
$d = 43°$ $e = 43°$
c) $m = 140°,$ $n = 140°, p = 134°,$
$q = 46°,$ $r = 40°$

Polygons P.60

Q1 Isosceles.

Q2

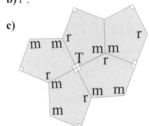

order of rotational symmetry = 6.

Q3 **a)** Angles at a point sum to 360°,
hence m + m + r = 360°.
Angles in a pentagon sum to 540°.
We know two angles are 90°, so we
are left with 360°. The only angles
left are m, m and r so m + m + r
must equal 360°.
b) r°.

c)

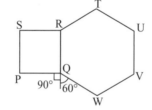

Q4 **a)** $90° + 60° = 150°$

b)

$\angle$PRW = 75°
c) $180 - (360/n) = 150$
$180n - 360 = 150n$
$30n = 360 \Rightarrow n = 12$

Q5 $540° - (100° + 104° + 120°)$
$= 216°$ for two equal angles
$\therefore 1$ angle $= 108°$

Q6 **a)** Interior angle = 165°
b) Exterior angle $= 180° - 165° = 15°$
Sum of exterior angles $= 15 \times 24$
$= 360°$

Symmetry P.61-P.62

Q1

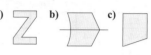

a)   **b)**   **c)**

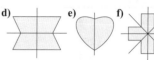

d)   **e)**   **f)**

Q2 **a)** 6   **b)** 8
c) 5   **d)** 3

Q3

1   2   1   1

Order of Rotation

1   1   2

Q4 No

Q5 Four. Three like this:

and one through its middle:

Q6 Infinitely many.

Q7 No

Q8 One of the following:

Q9 A point

Q10 **a)** Two, one longitudinal and one
perpendicular to that.
b) 90°
c) They meet in a line.

Q11 **a)** 4
b) Yes it is true.

Circle Geometry P.63-P.64

Q1 **a)** BAD = 80° (opposite angle C in
cyclic quadrilateral)
b) EAB = 180 – 80 – 30 = 70°

Q2 **a)** BD = 5 cm (as the tangents BD and
CD are equal).
b) Angle COD = 70° (= 180° – (20° +
90°)), since the tangent CD meets
the radius OC at an angle of 90°.
c) Angle COB = 140° (since angle
BOD equals angle COD).
d) Angle CAB = 70° (since the angle at
the centre (COB) is twice the angle
at the edge (CAB)).

Q3 a) BOE = 106° (angle at centre)
b) ACE = 32° (angle in opposite segment)

Q4 a) ACD = 70° (angle in opposite segment)
b) BAD = 180 – (30 + 70) = 80° (opposite angles of a cyclic quadrilateral total 180°)

Q5 a) Angles in the same segment.
b) $3x + 40 = 6x - 50$
$90 = 3x$
$30 = x$
angle ABD = 3(30) + 40 = 130°

Q6 There are 2 ways of answering this question.

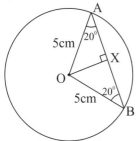

The perpendicular bisector of the chord bisects it at X so,
$\cos 20° = \frac{AX}{5}$ =>
AX = 4.698 and
AB = 9.40 cm.

or by the sine rule $\frac{AB}{\sin 140} = \frac{5}{\sin 20}$
AB = $\frac{5 \sin 140}{\sin 20}$ = 9.40 cm

Q7 a) Angle ABD = 70° (angle at centre = 2 × angle at circumference)
b) Angle ABC = 90° (angle in semicircle)
c) Angle DBC = 20° (90° – 70°)

Q8 a) 90° (angle in a semicircle)
b) The angle at A = 90° (tangent and radius are perpendicular). The third angle in the triangle is 180 – 90 – 23 = 67° and so $x = 90 - 67 = 23°$.
Or, by alternative segment theorem: x = angle ABC = 23°.

Q9 a) With AD as a chord, angle ABD = ACD = 30° (same segment); angle AXB = 85° (vertically opposite angles). The third angles must be the same in both triangles so the triangles must be similar.
b) Ratio of lengths = $\frac{4}{8} = \frac{1}{2}$ so XB = 7.25 cm
c) angle BDC = 180 – 85 – 30 = 65°

Q10 a) 90° (angle in a semicircle)
b) Pythagoras is needed here but in the form
$AC^2 + 3^2 = 10^2$
$AC^2 = 100 - 9 = 91$
AC = 9.54 cm
c) AD = 5 cm so DC = 9.54 – 5 = 4.54 cm then Pythagoras again gives
$(4.54)^2 + 3^2 = (DOB)^2$
$20.606 + 9 = (DOB)^2$
So DOB = 5.44 cm

The Four Transformations P.65-P.66

Q1 a) to e) — see diagram.

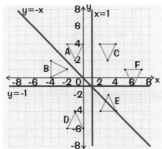

f) Rotation of 180°, centre (3, 0)

Q2 a), b), d), e) — see diagram

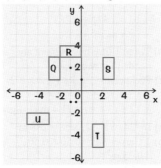

c) Rotation 180° about (0, 2).
f) 90° rotation anticlockwise about $\left(-\frac{1}{2}, -\frac{1}{2}\right)$.

Q3 a), b) — see diagram.

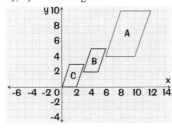

c) Ratio of areas C:A = 1:4

Q4 a), b), c) — see diagram.

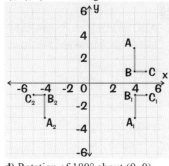

d) Rotation of 180° about (0, 0)

Enlargements P.67

Q1 a) & b)

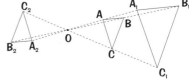

Q2 a) 2 end faces 2 × (2 × 3) = 12 cm²
2 side faces 2 × (5 × 3) = 30 cm²
Top & bottom 2 × (5 × 2) = 20 cm²
Total = 62 cm²
b) SF for length = 1:4
SF for area = 1:16
new area = 62 × 16 = 992 cm²

Q3 Widths in ratio 2:3, so volumes in ratio 8:27.
Volume = $30 \times \frac{27}{8}$ = 101 litres

Q4 a) volume = $\frac{1}{3}\pi(100^2)(100)$
= 1047198 cm³
= 1.05 m³
b) 50 cm
c) ratio = $1:2^3$ = 1:8
d) Volume of small cone = $1.05 \times \frac{1}{8}$ = 0.131 m³
e) volume of portion left = 1.05 – 0.131 = 0.919
so ratio = 0.919:0.131 = $\frac{0.919}{0.131}$:1 = 7:1

Answers: P.68 — P.72

Congruent and Similar Shapes P.68

Q1 ABC and DFE are congruent by SAS (same size angles and side lengths).

Q2
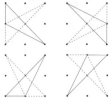
Hence 7 ways to draw <u>another</u>.

Q3
a) Angle A shared. Parallel lines make corresponding angles equal so the triangles are similar by AAA.
b) Ratio of lengths given by
$\frac{AB}{AD} = \frac{12}{20} = \frac{3}{5}$
So $x = 25 \times \frac{3}{5} = 15$ cm
Also $\frac{y + 10}{y} = \frac{5}{3}$
$=> 2y = 30,\ y = 15$ cm

Q4
a) Triangles APQ and STC (both isosceles and share either angle A or C)
b) Ratio AC:AQ = 24:7.5 = 3.2:1 so
AP = $15 \times \frac{1}{3.2} = 4.6875$ cm
PT = $24 - 2 (4.6875)$
= 14.625 cm.
c) Using $\frac{1}{2}$(base)(height)
= $\frac{1}{2}(24)(9) = 108$ cm²
d) Scale factor = $\frac{1}{3.2}$
Area scale factor = $\frac{1}{10.24}$
Area of triangle APQ = $108 \times \frac{1}{10.24} = 10.5$ cm²
e) $108 - 2 (10.5) = 87$ cm²

Q5
a) All lengths must be enlarged in the same ratio for them to be similar.
b) 4 litres

Projections P.69

Q1
a) Front elevation:

b) Side elevation:

c) Plan:

Q2

Q3

4 cm | 5 cm
6 cm

Q4

Plan view

Front elevation   Side elevation

Perimeter and Area P.70-P.71

Q1 Area 24 cm², perimeter 20 cm

Q2 Area 25 cm², perimeter 20 cm

Q3
a) Area = (4×4)
$- (1 \times 2 + \frac{1}{2} \times \pi \times 1^2)$
$+ \frac{1}{2} \times \pi \times 2^2$
$= 16 - 3.571 + 6.283$
$= 18.7$ m² (1 d.p.)
b) Three 1 litre tins of paint are needed for two coats.
c) Perimeter = $1 + 1 + (\frac{1}{2} \times \pi \times 2)$
$+ 1 + 1 + 4 + (\frac{1}{2} \times \pi \times 4) + 4$
$= 12 + (3 \times \pi) = 21.4$ m (1 d.p.)

Q4
a) l = 24, w = 12, area = 288 m²
b) 1 Carpet tile = 0.50×0.50
= 0.25 m²
So 288 m² ÷ 0.25 = 1152 tiles are required.
c) £4.99 per m² => £4.99 for 4 tiles
Total cost = (1152 ÷ 4) × 4.99
= £1437.12

Q5 Area = 120 cm²

Q6 Each square = 0.6 m × 0.6 m = 0.36 m².
Total area of material = $6 \times 0.36 = 2.16$ m².

Q7 Perimeter = $4 \times \sqrt{9000}$
= 379.47 m (2 d.p.)
Natasha ran: 11 × 379.47
= 4200 m (to nearest 100 m)

Q8
a) Area = area of a full circle radius 10 cm. A = $\pi r^2 = \pi \times 10^2$
= 314.2 cm² (1 d.p.).
Circumference = $\pi \times D = \pi \times 20$
= 62.8 cm.
Perimeter = 62.8 + 20 = 82.8 cm (1 d.p.).

b) Area = (area of a full circle radius 15 cm) + (area of a rectangle 15×30 cm) = $(\pi \times 15^2) + (15 \times 30)$
= 1156.9 cm² (1 d.p.)
Perimeter = (Circumference of a full circle radius 15 cm) + 15 + 15 (two shorter sides of rectangle)
= $(\pi \times 30) + 30 = 124.2$ cm (1 d.p.).
c) Area = Outer semi circle – Inner semi circle = 510.51 m². Perimeter
= ½ Circumference of larger
+ ½ Circumference of inner + 5 + 5
= $\frac{1}{2} \times \pi \times 70 + \frac{1}{2} \times \pi \times 60 + 10$
= 214.2 m (1 d.p.).

Q9 $80/360 \times \pi(5)^2 = 17.45$ cm²

Q10 Area of larger triangle = $\frac{1}{2} \times 14.4 \times 10$
= 72 cm².
Area of inner triangle = $\frac{1}{2} \times 5.76 \times 4$ = 11.52 cm².
Area of metal used for a bracket = $72 - 11.52 = 60.48$ cm².
No, the fixing will not take the weight of the bracket.

Q11 T_1: $\frac{1}{2} \times 8 \times 16 = 64$ m²
Tr_1: $\frac{1}{2} \times 8 \times (8 + 16) = 96$ m²
Tr_2: $\frac{1}{2} \times 4 \times (8 + 12) = 40$ m²
T_2: $\frac{1}{2} \times 8 \times 12 = 48$ m²
Total area of glass sculpture = 248 m²

Q12
a) Area of each isosceles triangle
= $\frac{1}{2} \times 2.3 \times 3.2 = 3.68$ m²
b) Area of each side =
$3.4 \times 4 = 13.6$ m²
Groundsheet = $2.3 \times 4 = 9.2$ m²
c) Total material = $2 \times 3.68 + 9.2 + 2 \times 13.6 = 43.8$ m²

Q13
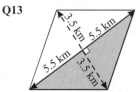
Area = area of two triangles:
= 2(½ × base x height)
= 2(½ × 11 × 3.5) = 38.5 km².

Surface Area P.72-73

Q1 a) - c)
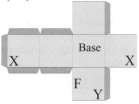

Q2

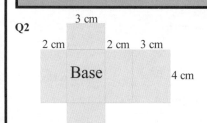

Other arrangements are possible.

Q3 **a)** H, F and D
b) Line symmetry through lines AF, DH, BG and CE. Rotational symmetry of order 4.
c) 5 faces and vertices, 8 edges.

Q4 **a)** I
b) 64 cm²
c) 64 × 6 = 384 cm²
d)

Q5 Net B

Q6 No, Hannah would need more than 603 cm².

Q7 Surface area = 4 × π × 3²
= 113.10 cm² (to 2 d.p)

Q8 Surface area of cone = $\pi rl + \pi r^2$
= (π × 1.5 × 8) + (π × 1.5²)
= 44.77 cm² (to 2 d.p)
Height of triangular prism =
$\sqrt{3^2 - 1.5^2} = \sqrt{6.75}$ = 2.598... cm
Surface area of triangular prism =
$2(\frac{1}{2} × 3 × 2.598...) + 3(3 × 8)$
= 79.79 cm² (to 2 d.p.)

Therefore the triangular prism has the largest surface area.

Q9 Surface area of hemisphere =
$\pi r^2 + \frac{1}{2}(4\pi r^2)$
$75\pi = 3\pi r^2$
$r^2 = 25$, radius = 5 cm

Q10 AB² = 2² + 1.5² AB = 2.5 m
1 panel on roof = ½AB × $\frac{5}{2}$
= 1.25 × 2.5 = 3.125 m²
Front of greenhouse = (2.5 × 4) +
(½ × 4 × 1.5) = 13 m²
Total = 3.125 + 13 = 16.125 m²

Volume P.74-P.75

Q1 **a)** $\frac{1}{2}\pi(0.35)^2$ = 0.192 m²
b) 0.1924 × 3 = 0.577 m³

Q2 **a)** π(2.5² – 2²) = 7.07 m²
£16 × 7.07 = £113.12 = £110 to nearest £10.
b) Volume = π(2)² × 0.50 = 6.28 m³
so use 6.28 × 15 = 94 ml treatment to the nearest ml.

Q3 Volume Cube = Volume Cylinder
$10^3 = \pi r^2 × 10$ so $r^2 = \frac{10^2}{\pi}$,
r = 5.64 cm

Q4 **a)** π(5)²(16) = 1257 cm³
b) π(5)²h = 600
$h = \frac{600}{25\pi}$ = 7.64 cm

Q5 (3)(3)(0.5) – π(0.7)²(0.5) = 3.73 cm³

Q6 (π ×(2)² × 110) +
(½(14 + 20) × 6 × 20) = 3422.30 cm³
2 × 3422.30 = 6844.60 cm³ = 6.84 l

Q7 **a)** (60)(30) + (30)(120) = 5400 cm²
b) 5400 × 100 = 540000 cm³ = 0.54 m³

Q8 Volume of ice cream

$= \frac{1}{3}\pi(R^2H - r^2h) + \frac{1}{2}(\frac{4}{3}\pi R^3)$

$= \frac{1}{3}\pi(2.5^2 × 10 - 1^2 × 4)$

$+ \frac{1}{2}(\frac{4}{3}\pi × 2.5^3)$

= 93.99 cm³ of ice cream.

Q9 Vol. increase is a cylinder of height 4.5 cm. So vol. increase =
π(5)² × 4.5 = 353.4 cm³.
Volume of each marble = $\frac{353.4}{200}$
= 1.767 cm³
$\frac{4}{3}\pi r^3$ = 1.767 => r = 0.75 cm

Speed, Distance and Time P.76

Q1 **a)** 98.9 mph (to 3 s.f.)
b) 72.56 seconds
c) 99.2 mph (to 3 s.f.)

Q2 **a)** 2.77 + 1.96 + 0.6 = 5.33 hrs
(to 3 s.f.) = 5 hours 20 mins
b) 250 miles
c) 46.9 mph (to 3 s.f.)

Q3 The first athlete ran at
16000 ÷ (60 × 60) = 4.44 m/s,
so was faster than the second athlete (at 4 m/s).
The first athlete would take 37.5 mins to run 10 km; the second would take 41.7 mins.

Q4 **a)** 487.5 km
b) 920.8 km
c) 497 km/h

Q5 **a)** 220 km
b) 5 mins

Q6 180 m at 42 mph takes 4 hrs 17 mins.
180 m at 64 mph takes 2 hrs 49 mins.
So it stops for 1 hr 28 mins.

Q7 **a)** 4.8 m/s
b) 14.4 m/s
c) 14.4 m/s
d) 17.3 km/h, 51.8 km/h, 51.8 km/h

Density P.77

Q1 **a)** 0.75 g/cm³
b) 0.6 g/cm³
c) 0.8 g/cm³
d) 700 kg/m³ = 0.7 g/cm³

Q2 **a)** 62.4 g
b) 96 g
c) 3744 g (3.744 kg)
d) 75 g

Q3 **a)** 625 cm³
b) 89.3 cm³ (to 3 s.f.)
c) 27778 cm³ (27800 to 3 s.f.)
d) 2500 cm³

Q4 34.71 g

Q5 20968 cm³

Q6 Vol. = 5000 cm³ = 5 litres

Q7 1.05 g/cm³

Q8 **a)** SR flour 1.16 g/cm³; granary flour 1.19 g/cm³
b) 378 ml

Distance-Time Graphs P.78-P.79

Q1 **a)** 4 km
b) 15 mins and 45 mins
c) 2.4 km/h
d) 1100
e) 10 km/h
f) 1030

Q2 **a)** 85 mins
b) 80 mins
c) 16.9 mph
d) 57.6 mph
e) No, because the total driving time is 80 minutes.

Q3

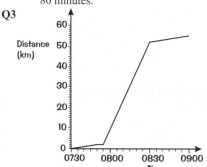

He waited for 5 mins.

Q4 **a)** A 80.0 km/h, fastest.
B 57.1 km/h
C 66.7 km/h
D 44.4 km/h
E 50.0 km/h
b) steepest slope was fastest, least steep slope was slowest.

Answers: P.79 — P.84

Q5 **a)** B

b) 3¾ mins

c) B

d) i) 267 m/min **ii)** 16.0 km/h

e) C was the fastest;
700 m/min or 42 km/h

Q6 **a)**

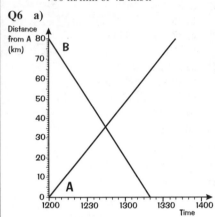

b) accept 1243-1245

c) accept 35-36 km

Q7 **a)**

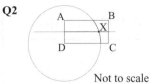

b) 25.75 km

c) 3.68 km/h

d) Her fastest speed was in the first
section (steepest graph) — her
speed was 5.14 km/h.

Velocity-Time Graphs P.80

Q1 **a) i)** 90 km

ii) 150 km

b) 320 km

Q2 **a) i)** 17.5 km

ii) 50 km

b) 102.5 km

Q3 **a)** 140 m

b) 10 m/s²

Q4 **a)** Approximately 117 m

b) Approximately 5-6 m/s²

Unit Conversions P.81

Q1 **a)** 200 cm **i)** 6000 mm

b) 33 mm **j)** 0.002 kg

c) 4000 g **k)** 3 kg

d) 0.6 kg **l)** 86 mm

e) 0.65 km **m)** 5500 g

f) 9000 g **n)** 354 cm

g) 0.007 kg **o)** 7 mm

h) 0.95 kg

Q2 147 kg × 2.2 = 323.4 lbs

Q3 14 gallons = 14 × 4.5 = 63 litres

Q4 59.1 kg

Q5 Barry cycled 30 miles = 30 × 1.6 =
48 km. So Barbara cycled furthest.

Q6 **a)** 11 in = 11 × 2.5 = 27.5 cm

b) 275 mm

Q7 **a)** 21 feet = 21 × 12 = 252 in

b) 21 feet = 21 ÷ 3 = 7 yd

c) 252 in = 252 × 2.5 = 630 cm

d) 630 cm = 6.3 m

e) 630 cm = 6300 mm

f) 6.3 m = 0.0063 km

Q8 5 lb = 5 ÷ 2.2 = 2.3 kg (1 d.p.).
So Dick needs to buy <u>3 bags</u> of sugar.

Q9 **a)** £148.65 **g)** £81.50

b) £62.19 **h)** £13.51

c) £679.18 **i)** £272.65

d) £100 **j)** £307.25

e) £1.36 **k)** £408.16

f) £795.92 **l)** £0.68

Conversion Graphs P.82

Q1 **a)** £5

b) £9.50

c) £17

d) No (Each 4.5 mile journey costs
more than £8)

Q2 **a)** 12-13 miles

b) 43-44 miles

c) 56-57 miles

Q3 **a)** 63-65 km

b) 15-17 km

c) 47-49 km

Loci and Construction P.83-P.84

Q1

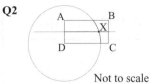

Not to scale

Q2

Not to scale

Q3 **a) and b)**

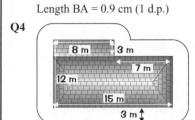

Not to scale

Length BA = 0.9 cm (1 d.p.)

Q4

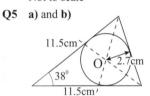

Not to scale

Q5 **a) and b)**

Not to scale
Radius of the circle = 2.7 cm

Q6 **a)** A circle with diameter AB.

b) and c)

Not to scale

d) The ship comes 1.7 cm = 0.85 km
from the rocks.

Q7

DOOR

WINDOW — 4 m

1.5 m

2 m

RADIATOR

5 m

Not to scale

Q8 **a)**

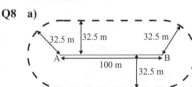

32.5 m 32.5 m   32.5 m
A   100 m   B
32.5 m

b) Distance around dashed path =
(2 × 100) + (π × 65) = 404.2 m

Q9

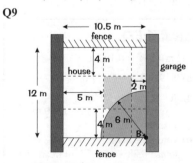

Not to scale

SECTION FOUR — GEOMETRY AND MEASURE

Answers: P.84 — P.89

Q10 a)

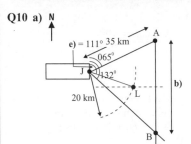

b) Length = 8.6 cm equivalent to 43 km.
c) 35 km in 2.5 hrs, so speed $= \frac{35}{2.5} = 14$ km/h.
d) and **e)** see diagram

Bearings P.85

Q1 a) 245°
b) 310°
c) 035°
d) 131°
e) 297°, 028°, 208°

Q2 a)

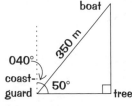

i) 268 m
ii) 225 m
b) $350^2 = 122\ 500$.
$225^2 + 268^2 = 122\ 449$

Q3

a) 96 km
b) 255 km
c) 266 km
d) 156°
e) 082°
f) 177°

Q4

start)165°
1200 m
210°
1500 m
finish
2500 m, 010°

Section Five —
Pythagoras and
Trigonometry
Pythagoras' Theorem
P.86-P.87

Q1 a) 10.8 cm
b) 6.10 m
c) 5 cm
d) 27.0 mm
e) 8.49 m
f) 7.89 m
g) 9.60 cm
h) 4.97 cm
i) 6.80 cm
j) 8.5 cm

Q2 a = 3.32 cm
b = 6 cm
c = 6.26 m
d = 5.6 mm
e = 7.08 mm
f = 8.62 m
g = 6.42 m
h = 19.2 mm
i = 9.65 m
j = 48.7 mm

Q3 k = 6.55 cm
l = 4.87 m
m = 6.01 m
n = 12.4 cm
p = 5.22 cm
q = 7.07 cm
r = 7.50 m
s = 9.45 mm
t = 4.33 cm
u = 7.14 m

Q4 AB: 5 (don't need Pythagoras)
CD: $\sqrt{10} = 3.16$
EF: $\sqrt{13} = 3.61$
GH: $\sqrt{8} = 2.83$
JK: $\sqrt{5} = 2.24$
LM: $\sqrt{26} = 5.10$
PQ: $\sqrt{20} = 4.47$
RS: $\sqrt{45} = 6.71$
TU: $\sqrt{13} = 3.61$

Q5 a) 12 cm, 7.94 cm
b) 40.9 cm
c) 89.7 cm^2

Q6 314 m

Q7 91.9 cm

Q8 5.0 m

Q9 4.58 m

Trigonometry — Sin, Cos, Tan
P.88-P.89

		(tan)	(sin)	(cos)
Q1	a)	0.306	0.292	0.956
	b)	8.14	0.993	0.122
	c)	0.0875	0.0872	0.996
	d)	0.532	0.469	0.883
	e)	1	0.707	0.707

Q2 a = 1.40 cm
b = 6 cm
θ = 28.1°
c = 5.31 cm
d = 10.8 cm

Q3 e = 12.6 cm
f = 11.3 cm
θ = 49.5°
g = 6.71 m
h = 30.1 cm

Q4 i = 4.89 cm
j = 3.79 cm
θ = 52.4°
k = 5.32 cm
l = 41.6 cm

Q5 m = 11.3 cm
n = 18.8 cm
p = 8.62 cm
q = 21.3 cm
r = 54.6°
t = 59.8 cm
u = 14.5 cm
v = 11.7 cm
w = 11.7 cm

Q6 a)

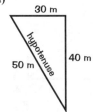

b) 36.9°

Q7 62°

Q8 20.5°

Answers: P.89 — P.92

Q9

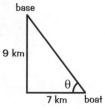

θ = 52.1°, bearing = 322°

Q10

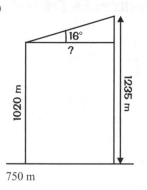

Q11

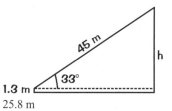

25.8 m

Q12

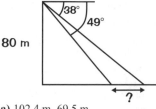

a) 102.4 m, 69.5 m
b) 32.9 m

Q13

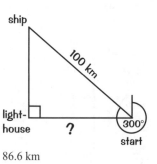

86.6 km

The Sine and Cosine Rules
P.90-P.91

Q1 $a = 4.80$ cm $f = 5.26$ cm
         $b = 25.8$ mm $g = 9.96$ cm
         $c = 13.0$ cm $h = 20.2$ mm
         $d = 8.89$ m $i = 3.72$ m
         $e = 18.4$ cm $j = 8.29$ cm

Q2 $k = 51°$ $q = 36°$
         $l = 46°$ $r = 64°$
         $m = 43°$ $s = 18°$
         $n = 88°$ $t = 49°$
         $p = 45°$

Q3 $a = 63°$ $f = 68°$
         $b = 45°$ $g = 203$ mm
         $c = 8.9$ cm $h = 127$ mm
         $d = 27°$
         $e = 10.5$ cm

Q4 **a)** 46°
         b) 52°   **c)** 82°

Q5 12.0 m

Q6

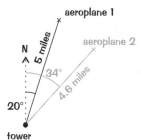

Distance = 1.2 miles.
The alarm should be ringing because
the planes are less than 3 miles apart,
so the software seems reliable.

Q7

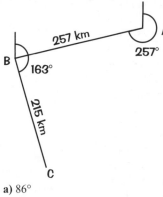

a) 86°
b) 323 km
c) 215°

Q8 **a)**

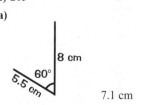

7.1 cm

---

b)

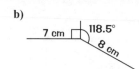

14.5 cm
(118.5° comes from the fact that the
minute hand is at 19.75 mins.
19.75 ÷ 60 × 360 = 118.5.)

c)

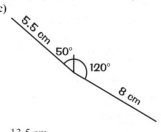

13.5 cm

Q9 Height of building = 35 m

3D Pythagoras and Trigonometry
P.92

Q1 **a)** 59.0°
         b) 23.3 cm
         c) 25 cm
         d) 21.1°

Q2 **a)** 42.5 cm
         b) 50.9 cm

Q3 **a)** 36.1 cm, 21.5 cm, 31.0 cm
         b) 36.9 cm

Q4 **a)** 15.4 cm
         b) 20.4 cm

Q5 The 85p box

Q6 **a)** 3.82 cm
         b) 45.8 cm²
         c) 137.5 cm³

Answers: P.93 — P.100

Section Six — Statistics and Probability
Collecting Data P.93

Q1 **a)** E.g. the question is vague/ subjective – "very often" can mean different things to different people.

b) E.g. "How many times a week do you visit the school canteen?"

Q2 E.g. the question isn't relevant to what the council wants to find out.

Q3 **a)** Unsuitable — e.g. people may like every one of the desserts, and this wouldn't tell you which was their favourite.

b) Unsuitable — e.g. the question is not relevant.

c) Suitable — it is the only one which will always tell you which of the five desserts people like the most.

d) Unsuitable — e.g. question is too vague, so people may give answers which are not on the list of desserts.

Q4 **a)** E.g.

> **Café Questionnaire**
>
> 1) Please tick the box to show how often you visit the café:
>
> daily ☐ weekly ☐ fortnightly ☐
> monthly ☐ less than monthly ☐
>
> 2) Please tick the box to show how often you buy cola:
>
> daily ☐ weekly ☐ fortnightly ☐
> monthly ☐ less than monthly ☐

b) She will miss out the people who just buy drinks from the hot and cold drinks machines.

Mean, Median, Mode and Range P.94-P.95

Q1 3 tries

Q2 mean = 1.333 (to 3 dp)
median = 1.5
mode = 2
range = 11

Q3 **a)** mean = £12,944, or £13,000 to the nearest £500
median = £12,000
mode = £7,500

b) mode

c) E.g. mean — they should use the highest value to attract people to the job.

Q4 **a)** 0 minutes
b) 0 minutes
c) 0 minutes
d) No, according to the raw data.

Q5 73.5 kg

Q6 20 kg

Q7 97%

Q8 **a)** 22   **b)** 74

Q9 **a)** 3.5
b) 3.5   **c)** 5

Q10 **a)** Both spend a mean of 2 hours.
b) The range for Jim is 3 hours and for Bob is 2 hours.
c) The amount of TV that Jim watches each night is more variable than the amount that Bob watches.

Q11 **a)** 1 day
b) 2 days
c) The statement is true according to the data.

Q12 **a)** mode
b) median   **c)** mean

Averages and Spread P.96

Q1 **a)** 65 g
b) The 2nd quartile (or Q_2)

Q2 **a)** 1020 − 80 = 940
b) 510
c) 700
d) 840

Q3 200

Q4 **a)** 325   **b)** 50

Frequency Tables – Finding Averages P.97-P.98

Q1 **a)** 12   **b)** 12
c) 2

Q2 **a)**

Subject	M	E	F	A	S
Frequency	5	7	3	4	6

b) 36 French lessons   **c)** English

Q3

Length (m)	4 and under	6	8	10	12	14 and over
Frequency	3	5	6	4	1	1

a) 8 m   **b)** 8 m   **c)** 14 m

Q4

Weight (kg)	Frequency	Weight × Frequency
51	40	2040
52	30	1560
53	45	2385
54	10	540
55	5	275

a) 52 kg
b) 2 kg
c) 53 kg
d) 52 kg (to nearest kg)

Q5 mean = 3.75
mode = 3
median = 4

Q6 **a)** 4
b) 3   **c)** 3.2 (to 1 dp)

Q7 **a)** **i)** False, mode is 8.
ii) False, they are equal.
iii) True
b) **iv)**

Grouped Frequency Tables P.99

Q1 **a)**

Speed (km/h)	$40 \leqslant s < 45$	$45 \leqslant s < 50$	$50 \leqslant s < 55$	$55 \leqslant s < 60$	$60 \leqslant s < 65$
Frequency	4	8	10	7	3
Mid-Interval	42.5	47.5	52.5	57.5	62.5
Frequency × Mid-Interval	170	380	525	402.5	187.5

Estimated mean = 52 km/h
(to nearest km/h)

b) 22 skiers   **c)** 20 skiers

Q2 **a)**

Weight (kg)	Tally	Frequency	Mid-Interval	Frequency × Mid-Interval
$200 \leqslant w < 250$	IIII	4	225	900
$250 \leqslant w < 300$	ЖН	5	275	1375
$300 \leqslant w < 350$	ЖН II	7	325	2275
$350 \leqslant w < 400$	II	2	375	750

b) 294 kg (to nearest kg)
c) $300 \leqslant w < 350$ kg

Q3 **a)**

Number	$0 \leqslant n < 0.2$	$0.2 \leqslant n < 0.4$	$0.4 \leqslant n < 0.6$	$0.6 \leqslant n < 0.8$	$0.8 \leqslant n < 1$
Tally	ЖН ЖН II	ЖН I	ЖН ЖН II	ЖН ЖН	ЖН III
Frequency	12	6	12	10	8
Mid-Interval	0.1	0.3	0.5	0.7	0.9
Frequency × Mid-Interval	1.2	1.8	6	7	7.2

b) $0 \leqslant n < 0.2$ and $0.4 \leqslant n < 0.6$
c) $0.4 \leqslant n < 0.6$
d) 0.483 (3 dp)

Cumulative Frequency P.100

Q1 accept:
a) 133-134   **c)** 136-137
b) 127-128   **d)** 8-10

Q2 **a)**

Number of passengers	$0 \leqslant n < 50$	$50 \leqslant n < 100$	$100 \leqslant n < 150$	$150 \leqslant n < 200$	$200 \leqslant n < 250$	$250 \leqslant n < 300$
Frequency	2	7	10	5	3	1
Cumulative Frequency	2	9	19	24	27	28
Mid-Interval	25	75	125	175	225	275
Frequency × Mid-Interval	50	525	1250	875	675	275

Estimated mean = 130 passengers
(to nearest whole number)

Answers: P.100 — P.104

b)

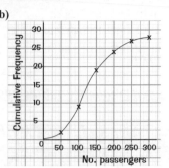

accept median of 118-122 passengers

c) $100 \le n < 150$

Q3 a)

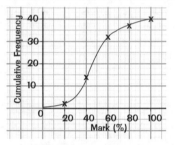

Mark (%)	$0 \le m < 20$	$20 \le m < 40$	$40 \le m < 60$	$60 \le m < 80$	$80 \le m < 100$
Frequency	2	12	18	5	3
Cumulative Frequency	2	14	32	37	40

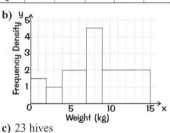

b) 36%-38%
c) 19%-21%
d) 45%-47%

Histograms and Frequency Density P.101-P.102

Q1 $4 \times 10 = 40$ people

Q2 a)

Weight (kg)	$0 \le w < 2$	$2 \le w < 4$	$4 \le w < 7$	$7 \le w < 9$	$9 \le w < 15$
Frequency	3	2	6	9	12
Frequency density	1.5	1	2	4.5	2

b)

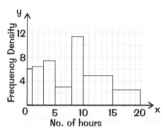

c) 23 hives

Q3 (A,I), (B,II)

Q4 a)

No. of hours	Frequency	Frequency density
$0 \le h < 1$	6	6
$1 \le h < 3$	13	6.5
$3 \le h < 5$	15	7.5
$5 \le h < 8$	9	3
$8 \le h < 10$	23	11.5
$10 \le h < 15$	25	5
$15 \le h < 20$	12	2.4

b) 103 students

c)

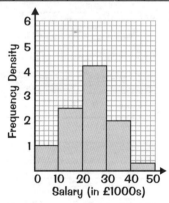

d) 41 students

Q5 A — 16 year olds

B — bags of sugar

Q6 a)

Salary (£1000s)	$0 \le s < 10$	$10 \le s < 20$	$20 \le s < 30$	$30 \le s < 40$	$40 \le s < 50$
Frequency	10	25	42	20	3
Frequency Density	1	2.5	4.2	2	0.3

b) E.g. there are more people with higher salaries now than 10 years ago.

Other Graphs and Charts P.103-P.104

Q1 $\dfrac{360°}{100} = 3.6°$ per gram

Carbohydrate $3.6 \times 35 = 126°$
Protein $3.6 \times 15 = 54°$
Fat $3.6 \times 10 = 36°$
Magical Fairy Dust $3.6 \times 40 = \underline{144°}$
                $360°$

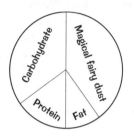

Q2 Sherrington 380,000 = 148° (approx)
2600 visitors = 1°
So, to the nearest 10,000:
Brompton = $2600 \times 118° \approx 310{,}000$
Barny = $2600 \times 44° \approx 110{,}000$
Livsea = $2600 \times 50° \approx 130{,}000$

Q3 Part **c)**

Q4 It's not possible to tell whether more people voted for the Green Party in 2009, because you can't tell how many people voted in either election.

Q5 a)

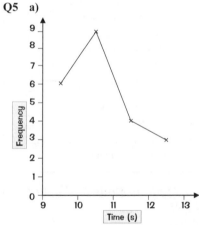

b) 22
c) 19

Q6 a)

Level of skier	No.
Beginner	⊬⊦ |||
Intermediate	⊬⊦ |||
Good	||||
Very good	|||
Racer	|||

Answers: *P.104 — P.108*

b)

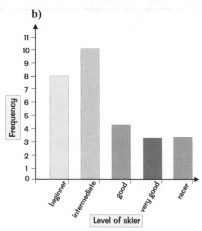

c) Most common type of skier is Intermediate.

Q7 The statement is not correct. Complaints have not "tailed off" — they have remained the same (approx 10,850) per month, so there's no evidence that the products are of a better quality.

Scatter Graphs P.105

Q1 A: labelled S
B: labelled R
C: labelled P
D: labelled U

Q2 a)

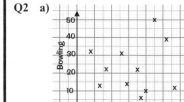

b) There is no correlation.
c) No — if he were correct the graph would show negative correlation.

Q3 a), b)

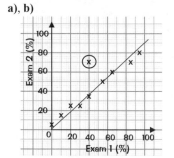

c) 46% (accept any answer between 40% and 50%)

Probability P.106-P.108

Q1 **a)** 1/2   **c)** 1/6
b) 2/3   **d)** 0

And so should be arranged <u>approximately</u> like this on the number line.

Guatemalan stamp — Five on a dice — 0 — 0.5 — Head on a coin — Red ball — 1

Q2 Debbie's chance of winning would be 1/9. This is greater than 0.1, so she would choose to play.

Q3 The probability of a head is still 1/2

Q4 1 − 0.27 = 0.73 or 73/100

Q5 **a)** 5/12   **c)** 3/12 = 1/4
b) 4/12 = 1/3   **d)** 9/12 = 3/4

Q6 **a)** 40/132 = 10/33
b) P(car being blue or green) = 45/132
P(not blue or green) = 87/132 = 29/44

Q7

	1	2	3	4	5
1	1,1	1,2	1,3	1,4	1,5
2	2,1	2,2	2,3	2,4	2,5
3	3,1	3,2	3,3	3,4	3,5
4	4,1	4,2	4,3	4,4	4,5
5	5,1	5,2	5,3	5,4	5,5
6	6,1	6,2	6,3	6,4	6,5

Q8 a)

Outcome	Frequency
W	8
D	5
L	7

b) The 3 outcomes are not equally likely.
c) 1/4
d) They are most likely to win.

Q9 **a)** $\frac{1}{13}$
b) $\frac{2}{39}$ **c)** $\frac{1}{36}$

Q10 **a)** $\frac{7}{12}$ **b)** $\frac{7}{12}$
c) The two events can both happen at the same time, since 3 is a white.

Q11 **a)** $\frac{2}{5}$
b) $\frac{4}{15}$ **c)** $\frac{2}{3}$

Q12 a)

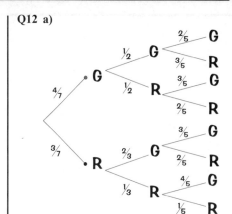

b) $\frac{18}{35}$
c) $\frac{3}{7}$

Q13 4 times

Q14 a)

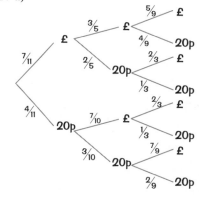

b) $\frac{28}{55}$ **c)** $\frac{46}{165}$

www.cgpbooks.co.uk